All Things Periods

Period Power Charity

All Things Periods

First paperback edition 2021

Edited by Eleanor Broadhurst

Artwork created by students from Trentham Academy, Stoke-on-Trent

Front cover created by Hannah Dickinson Rogers

Published in 2021 by North Staffordshire Press and Henson Editorial Services

North Staffordshire Press and Henson Editorial Services

Denise Coates Foundation Building

Keele

ST5 5NS

ISBN: 978-1-8384503-7-3

RRP £7.99

All Things Periods

Contents List

Period Power Charity

All Things Periods

FOREWORD

Period Power is a registered charity which was founded in September 2017. Since then, we have supported tens of thousands of women and girls with decent quality period products so that they can have a DIGNIFIED PERIOD.

However, we are also passionate in raising the issues surrounding period poverty and in removing the stigma surrounding periods. This book will, hopefully, encourage more and more women and girls to be open and honest about their "period experiences" so much so that these conversations become everyday conversations.

If you would like to learn more about the work we do please check us out on the following:

Website: www.periodpower.co.uk

Period Power @alallbutt

@PeriodPower2

periodpower2

Teen life periods:

Facts: you can still go swimming on your period (just use a tampon)

There are special kinds of pants for when you're on your period

Weather can affect your periods

You will spend around 10 years of your life on your period

Females' periods can synchronise so periods will start at the same time.

Menstrual Island:

Visit once a month and leave after 3~7 days.

Bloaty Town

Mountain of Pain

Mood Swings Lake

Crampy Valley

Sea of Blood

Princess Rukiya

The PersonalCare Bank

The PersonalCare bank is a hygiene, personal care provider. Among these products, we provide menstruation pads and tampons for pupils mainly from low-income households in schools. These families are served through their children, primarily by public donations of menstruation products. Our objective is to eliminate period poverty for period potential. DMee PersonalCare Bank is part of a registered, not-for-profit, organisation called Divine Ministries Education Enterprise (Nonprofit) Ltd.

Definitions of Low Income

Taking housing costs into account, in 2017-2018, there was an estimated 14 million people in the UK in relative low income (or 22% of the public)[1] and 12.5 million in absolute low income (or 19%)[2]. Working-age households on low income are likely to be in some kind of work. In 2017-2018, over half of low incomes households had at least one person in work. An estimated 4.1 million children live in a household in relative low income (30%), or 3.7 million in absolute low income (26%). About 70% of children in low incomes households have at least one person working[3].

Menstruation, the Impact of Surveys and Campaigning

In 2017, the charity Plan International UK carried out a survey of 1000 girls and women aged 14-21[4]. It demonstrated 1 in 10 girls cannot afford menstruation products. Plan International UK also found that half of all schoolgirls truanted a full day from school every month because of their period. Thus, I decided to focus the provision of menstruation pads and tampons for pupils requiring them from low-income families in schools, instead of a more general focus as was the case from 2016 to 2018 when I first started the PersonalCare Bank project.

Apart from surveys into Period Poverty, which is defined as 'people [or in this case, households] unable to afford menstruation products', since 2017, there have been countless provisions of period products to schools by charities such as Freedom4Girls, a Leeds charity which was established for women and girls in Kenya. However, in calls from Leeds Council for provision of menstruation to girls living in poverty, Freedom4Girls responded to local schools. The RedBox project, a national initiative, is another such charity. However, it was the joint strength of providers and the Free Period Movement – national, social activism which ultimately impacted change in period poverty for schools. The Free Period Movement took on a more feminist rather than income or socioeconomics, inequalities agenda and campaigned to remove the stigma associated with periods. They sought for it to be normalised as, menstruation is a natural, biological occurrence experienced by mainly females. Galvanising support from the public, the Free Period Movement won a legal case against the Government in 2019, which, from September 2019, English secondary schools were eligible to free period supplies. The same was granted to primary schools in September 2020. This Treasury promise aligned England with Scotland and Wales who, in 2017 and 2018 provided schools with state, free periods.

Whilst schools and colleges are entitled to a supply of free, state period products, funded through direct taxation, initial anecdotal evidence is showing that period poverty still remains and that the Government Free Period Scheme therefore does not eradicate period poverty in schools. This is because, for schools which have opted-into the Scheme, the yearly cap for each school is assessed on 35% of the total number of pupils at each school[5]. So, whilst all learners in schools and colleges up to age 19 are legally entitled to access free period products at their place of study, the policy does not account for the poor amongst these and for schools where a large number of children come from poor, low-income families.

Our schools, pupils, and families

From 2018, I started provision in Telford primary schools by connecting with local churches. However, from January 2019, I focused solely on Wolverhampton schools through partnership with Mac's Barbers – a local business which enabled storage of products and an outlet for promotion of the work. We serve Wolverhampton schools which educate disproportionate numbers of pupils from low-income families – as high as 4 out of 5 children are on free school meals in some schools. All schools are ethnically diverse, consisting also of refugee children. The student composition of the Telford schools represents the white, working class locally. The number of pupils on free school meals in these schools were similar to Wolverhampton.

All schools we are currently servicing have opted-into the Government Scheme. Nonetheless, the PersonalCare Bank continues to provide menstruation products to our schools for pupils from families on low incomes as long as stocks are available, and with support from partner charities such as Period Power, which is an invaluable assistance with our cause. Our provision of menstruation products thus supplements the giving of the Government Scheme. However, even with our help, we only service the most vulnerable at our schools.

Written by Professor Doreen W.McCalla

Every month I become a paranoid mess
Asking my nearest one to check the back of my dress
And you call it gross?
Let me remind you
You also started your life

Covered in your mother's blood
You may never understand what it feels like to bleed
Despite this entire curse
I always hold my head up high
And I succeed.

I will no longer hide that I am in pain
I will no longer be silent about my stain
I bleed to make humankind a possibility

I feel proud that it is a woman's most powerful ability
I bleed
I bleed
Yes, I bleed!

Written by Madi Hardy
The Discovery Academy, Bentilee, Stoke-on-Trent

Stomach cramps and mood swings.

We are always trying to stay clean

Pads and tampons to stop the flow

Even when you're down, there is a little hope

Stay close with your friends

Don't let your happiness come to an end

A little bit of chocolate with a hot water bottle

Will help your cravings for sugar and take your mind off the pain

It might be an uncomfortable few days and nights

But don't let people tell you we are the weaker gender

We may stay quiet, put our strong faces on

But about a week away from when you start the pain will be gone

So, treat yourself with some chocolate and a hot water bottle and chat with your friends to take your mind off the pain.

By a student from The Discovery Academy, Bentilee, Stoke-on-Trent

Where you can feel the pain:

Backaches, Headaches, Cramps.

Some people get sore shoulders.

We don't get to pick if we have periods or not.

We feel the pain for it emotionally and physically and yet we have to pay a lot of money just to get products.

We should follow Scotland and make these free.

Periods can make you feel many things like your emotions can get more intense, mood swings and this can happen at any time and can affect your day.

Physically, cramps and headaches are the two most common and can bring down your mood a lot.

By a student from The Discovery Academy, Bentilee, Stoke-on-Trent

Periods, periods,
Don't laugh at me,
It's normal for a girl,
NO! It's not red pee.
It affects me every month,
Sometimes more than others,
I hate it when I leak,
Cause I get laughed at by my brothers.
There are some boys out there,
Who won't laugh at you,
Take me for example,
I'm here to help you,
If you are bleeding,
Go to a friend,
They're here to help,
The world's not going to end,
It's not a girl's choice,
It is just life,
Why can't they live without an expensive price?
Get off your ass and come join me,
Period products should all be free.

By a student from The Discovery Academy, Bentilee, Stoke-on-Trent

Know thyself

I'm a professional interpreter working for the NHS. I get called for a plethora of cases where people speaking my mother tongue need a little help with understanding what the doctor says to them in English. But understanding the words isn't always the only problem. Turns out, around half of the women in the UK don't know what's exactly between their legs. This is 2021. In the United Kingdom. Cue giant facepalm.

People, we need to talk. I hope not only girls will read this but everyone else on the gender spectrum too, because it's important. It's important because if there's a problem, you need to be able to spot it and explain it to your doctor, or to send your partner for a check-up. It's important because while messing around with your partner, you might want to know what they mean by, say, the clitoris. And it's important because if you don't know what is normal, you may feel ashamed or self-conscious about your vulva and your reproductive system, and that's just not cool.

Right. Let's start with the period. Our womb is programmed to make babies. It is an unfortunate phenomenon that it expects us to make babies every damn month, but here we are. Unless you are in a loving relationship with stable finances and the robust support system of your family having your back, chances are you don't want a baby yet; you use contraception, likely condoms. (I don't even have to say that "taking it out" and "counting the days" aren't reliable methods, right?!) Your womb makes a nice and cosy place for the potential embryo to nestle into, but there's nothing! And so, the lining of the womb that awaited the baby sheds off, possibly causing you cramps and pains, and leaves your body in the form of your period. Your womb then starts building up its lining again, hoping that when you ovulate, this time there will be a fertilised egg to nurture.

That's it. Period blood is just uterine tissue. It's not dirty or unclean; just make sure you change your pads/tampons/cups regularly.

This whole process involves a lot of hormonal changes. Yes, we women are prone to turning into monsters towards the end of our menstrual cycle, before our menstruation starts. This is caused by our oestrogen levels plummeting and progesterone levels rising. The feelings we go through and the physical symptoms we experience (like bloating and acne) are caused by very real, hormonal changes in our body. Shaming us for it doesn't help, gentlefolk, so let's not use the phrase "she's PMSing" in a hurtful manner. And just a reminder that male contraception was abandoned because the dudes couldn't put up with the side effects messing with their hormones caused – like mood swings, anxiety, depression, and acne. Women deal with the exact same stuff every month, so show some respect, gentlefolk, and hand us a hot water bottle and a cup of cocoa while you are at it.

There are a number of myths around periods. I trust today's generation to be able to tap away on their smartphones and google them, so I'd like to assign just that as your homework. You'll find many easily digestible and dare I say, entertaining lists. I'll also leave you with some words for body parts that I think are important to know. Look them up on Google; see pictures so you can identify them clearly. Research how the menstrual cycle works and educate people around you – regardless of gender. Ready? Here we go.

Period Power Charity

Vulva

Clitoris

Inner and outer Labia

Urethral opening

Vaginal opening

Anus

Vagina

Cervix

Uterus

Womb

Ovaries

Fallopian tube

Oestrogen

Progesterone

Menstrual cycle

Bonus point: google what NASA asked Sally Ride, the first American female astronaut, about tampons. Cue giant facepalm. Don't be like NASA.

Written by Katalin Patnaik

"It's all part of growing," they say.
"You're turning into a young lady!" they smile
As the dull ache permeates through to my back and legs.
"It's all natural" they say
As the energy drains and my skin begins to burn.
I didn't want to be a young lady at 12.
If being a young lady is washing the stains from my pants,
If being a young lady is fearing leakage and being spotted
carrying pads in my pocket.
Don't let the boys steal them and throw them around!
What cheek burning humiliation.
Always got to be on guard when you are a young lady.
Learn how to carry things discretely, securely, in your hand or
pocket.

"What do you mean you need the toilet right now? Why didn't
you go at break?"
Because I couldn't spend that long in the cubicle
When 10 other girls were crowding to empty
Their bladders in the 10 minutes between lessons.
Can't let them hear the crumple of cellophane
"Are you on your period!" My cheeks grow crimson.

The bleeding started... way before any of my friends.
They were still children, they didn't know what I had to do,
They laughed at me,
They didn't understand why I didn't feel like running around the
playground

When my stomach feels like I have swallowed a bowling ball.
Then the blood flow became so heavy, a pad wouldn't last a
morning.
Constant fear, constant wet, constant fatigue.

Period Power Charity

"Oh, they will settle" you are just young.
Now run along, put on your short skirt, and jump in the air after
that ball.

When they started coming every 2 weeks,
The injustice ripped through me
Sharper than the tearing of the lining of my uterus.
The fear of using the toilet, the fear of leaking,
the pain, the exhaustion is overwhelming.
Difficult to focus on your course work.
"Concentrate – it will affect your overall score."

I can't go shopping with mum anymore.
She reads the prices of the pads whilst I walk away hanging my
head, cheeks burning,
She buys the special offer, the cheapest
Or drops into pound store to manage the budget.
Cos let's face it super heavy menstruation every 2 weeks
Kinda costs a lot.

Eventually I am given some tablets from the GP
"These will help her to regulate
She won't have to worry again."
But they didn't.

Time for my ballet exam.
"No pants under those leotards girls!"
Guess who wanted to join me on the day?
Ruin my chances of a career,
Spreading its pain and fatigue,
Challenging my concentration,
My strength,
My will to live

Whilst I am expected to look like grace, beauty, and light itself.

Back to the GP
More tablets. Didn't work
More tablets.
"If these don't work, we will have to think about the pill."

But Oh God that will make me fat.

Written by Olivia

We bleed, we rule.

"My Auntie has come to visit"
"The painters are in"
"Russia is invading"
"I'm waiting for the girly time to begin"

"LFC are at home"
"It's shark week I'm afraid"
"The crimson tide is turning"
"Mother nature's trick has been played"

Because it's embarrassing to speak it out loud
It's the bodily function that dare not say its name
We can't make others uncomfortable
So, we play "guess the period game"

And although our wombs are on fire
And our skin is running riot
We have a duty not to mention such things
And remain calm and quiet

We must not be over emotional
(Or be emotional at all, if that's okay?)
Mustn't show over sensitivity
Or even just have an "off day"

BUT

I can run my own business
A country if I need
And can chair a meeting
Whilst all the time I bleed

Yes I'm on my period,
Here are the pads I need
I'm not going to put them in a pretty bag
Or hide them up my sleeve

We can do it all sisters
We run, we rule, we achieve
We are no slaves to our hormones
As others may want us to believe

If my bleeding offends you
Tough. That sucks for you, my friend
It's not something to be ashamed of
This "period game" is at an end

So, let's reclaim OUR PERIOD
Let this be our finest hour
I bleed for a week whilst doing ALL THIS
What's your superpower?

Written by Jayne Kinsella

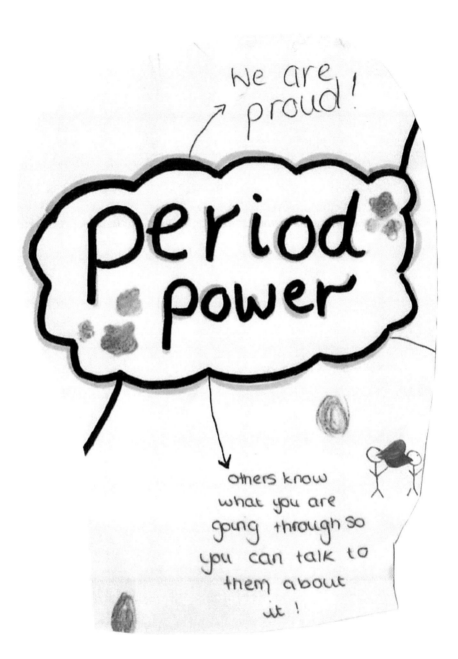

I was 13 years old
When I started to ache
My back and my stomach
Felt like they were in flames

I shouted for my mom
Sat covered in blood,
She didn't really explain
As much as I thought she would

She threw a pack of pads
On the bathroom floor
And awkwardly instructed me
From behind the closed door

I felt so embarrassed
Didn't know what to say
I guess it was just expected of me
To learn everything that day

I thought I knew everything...
From the puberty lesson in year 6
Is discharge normal?
And should it be heavy like this?

I thought I knew everything?!
I had the puberty lesson in school!
I swear they told me
I should only lose a teaspoon.

Period Power Charity

Heart pumping out my chest
And my cheeks were bright red
I forgot my pads at school
And I had to ask a friend

She threw me a tube of plastic
"This isn't a pad?"
I looked at her all confused
She thought I'd gone mad

"It's a tampon" she said
And I nodded, like I knew
Awkwardly trying to figure it out
I didn't have a clue

We were in year 9 after all
Shouldn't I know this by now?
I'm a woman after all...
I can't ask how!

It's expected of young girls
To know EXACTLY what to expect
Birthing hips and bright red lips
I wish somebody had checked

Because how was I supposed to ask
When it's such a taboo subject?
Didn't want anyone at school
To think I was a reject

I'm now 25 years old
With a daughter of my own
And I vow that she will never
Feel like she's on her own

And when she starts her period
I will make sure to say
TALKING ABOUT YOUR PERIOD
IS TOTALLY OKAY!

Written by Gemma Silwood

A letter to my Mum

Mum, I forgive you. You didn't teach me about my blood. About my body. But I understand. You were afraid, you felt the words were unspeakable. You stood with me in the darkness of shame. Together, yet alone. You shied away from the truth. The red menace attacked me at 10. And then I was a woman? And you had to accept all this and juggle your own emotions, your own fears. In the silence we parted. Separate, yet the same. And for me, I had become a woman. So undignified. So unaccepted. It stopped me in my tracks. I had monthly bouts of pain, tiredness, shame. I did not want to be this pathetic painful woman. I was free, fluid, flying and now? Now I am chained. Chained to my gender, chained to the toilet. Cursed. For what? For being a woman, for bleeding, for reproduction.

I forgive you Dad. You stood disgusted. No words to utter to me. No words of support or encouragement. Silent, like a stone. Strong and loving yet silent. And my brothers, I forgive you. You may have teased me, you may have mocked my pain, mocked my drained body. But in a world without forgiveness, we will just continue with the same old patterns. I say no. I am forging new pathways. I am daring into new worlds.

Finally, I forgive me, my personal self. I forgive me for my confusion. I forgive me for my seclusion, for my silence, for my shadows that followed me round and became my comfort zone.

So now, I have decided that I will stand proud, and I will stand loud. I will stand with you, my mother. I will stand with other women who bleed. I will stand with my father, with my brothers and together we shall speak the unspeakable.

I have a body that bleeds. I bleed for reproduction; I bleed to cleanse.

I have a body that bleeds. My blood speaks to me. My blood utters words of remembrance, words of letting go, words to heal, words to ground me, right now, in the present.

I have a body that bleeds. My blood releases my emotions. Through my shadows, I intimately connect with myself. A power exists within me to regenerate, to work with my cyclic nature.

I have a body that bleeds. My blood connects me to my cycle to empower me to deal with all the situations that present themselves to me.

I have a body that bleeds. My body is sacred. My body is beautiful. My cycles are emancipatory.

When my body bleeds, I venture inside to embark on a journey into the self, weaving worlds, crossing boundaries. Speaking in pride without fear of the darkness. Walking hand in hand, with the glory of imperfection.

Written by Aimee Blease-Bourne

The average number of periods in a lifetime and why humans are different

I recently worked out that the average number of periods in a lifetime = 468 (if an individual has regular periods between puberty and menopause). These were my rough calculations:

Since periods start at age 12 on average, and menopause starts at age 51 on average.

51-12= 39 years of periods

39 years x 12 monthly periods = 468 periods in a lifetime

Even if a woman has one child, the number goes down to 459 (468-9 months) or 450 after two children, so many women still have around 450 unneeded periods even if they have kids. Unless a woman has the maximum number of kids in her lifetime, 52 (468/9 months=52), she still doesn't need a period every single month. The human body should really have evolved to stop building up the uterine lining 'just in case' of fertilisation.

All mammals have menstrual cycles, but only a few species have periods. Most of these species have a very thin uterine lining that the body reabsorbs so there is no bleeding, and those who bleed only do so a small amount without the cramps and PMS symptoms that humans experience.

Some examples of animals that do bleed: apes, old world monkeys, bats, shrews, and the spiny mouse (more info here: https://emborawild.com/animals-that-menstruate/).

But humans grow the thickest uterine lining and bleed the most. Other species may have cycles that lead to regular mating seasons and/or times in heat but none of the bleeding. The fact that most species have periods of fertility without the level of discomfort that humans experience shows that humans could have evolved the same way.

However, humanity has stopped evolving. I think this is because we tend to invent man-made objects and devices to mitigate our flaws. Humanity wouldn't survive in the wild without clothes and tools, but animals are naturally equipped with features adapted to their climate, e.g., claws, venom, and fur.

So, most animals continue to evolve to adapt to a changing world, while humans tend to create objects to make things easier on themselves. Our bodies haven't altered or developed new features in a long time, so we still have some flaws like the unnecessary discomfort of periods. I've always found cramps and periods really inconvenient, so realising that humans could have gone without them was pretty frustrating.

The good thing about human's industrial nature is that we have created things like birth control and painkillers that can improve uncomfortable symptoms or stop periods altogether, which allows people to tailor their cycles to their personal preferences. So even though we haven't evolved in an ideal way, we have more control over our periods than other species do. At least that provides a little comfort when cramps come calling!

Written by Ewura- Ama Quarshie

When I was 13 I started experiencing menorrhagia and consulted a doctor about the discomfort it was causing me. I was shocked to be handed a plethora of pills; "if the norethisterone doesn't work, here's tranexamic acid." When that didn't work, "let's give mefenamic acid a go!" Unfortunately, I even ended up on a drip of some of these medications and was very sick as a result. I finally ended up on a mini pill to try to relieve these bothersome symptoms and I had a non-stop bleed for 6 whole months, being told, often by male doctors, that I just had to "persevere" and "give it a bit longer".

Obviously, this was a difficult period for me, not just due to the discomfort of menstruation for that long but also feeling that I wasn't being taken seriously and the effect that contraceptive pills can have on your emotions. Despite suspecting there was a hormonal root to my problems, I was told that getting a referral to endocrinology would be "useless" as "young girls' hormones are crazy even in normal cases!" Ironically, it was after pushing for a referral that I finally got definite answers!

Luckily, my issues have settled down since finding that an underactive thyroid was causing my symptoms, but I really hope that, in the future, more people begin to speak about how uncommon these rather difficult situations are. Sometimes, the healthcare profession needs to have more understanding about young people's experiences with puberty, and how some can struggle immensely with it even though others will fly through, and not automatically resort to drugs just because it may be easier than looking for another underlying cause in young people with fluctuating hormone levels.

Written by Sophie F

I always feel a bit guilty when reading of women and girls having a rough time with their period. I had 4 kids between the age of 18 and 28 and then had a coil fitted when I was 30 and haven't had a period since; only occasionally when I was flying long haul – very strange.

"Fanny Frock" – I was sitting next to a mate in the doctors – Emmie – she was 80 at the time. "What are you doing here?" I asked. In time honoured tradition she mimed "I'm having bloody mither down there" and pointed down. There was a bit of sign language, raised eyebrows and 'bloodys' with Emmie – I knew the language, so I got the drift. She then said, "I've even got to wear a bloody fanny frock." "You what duck?" I said. "You know, a bloody fanny frock" she replied. I had no idea what Em was on about. "What the hell's that duck?" I asked.

Em just looked at me gone out – "you know, a bloody pad" again said in mime. She then folded her arms – just like Les Dawson used to do when playing Cissy & Ida with Roy Barraclough – looked at me and tutted as if to say, "she knows nowt, that one."

Written by Rose

Since I have so many thoughts and feelings to do with my period, and since I can't find a good way to present it all in an artistic way, I think I'll just have to simply say it.

The thing I always dreaded most about puberty was my period. Just the idea of having to deal with blood coming out of my vagina among everything else really bothered me. I also knew I would get it early, since my mum had.

When I did get my period, I felt really alone. I didn't have any friends who had their period, and I felt really pressured by my mum to celebrate the fact that every month I'd have to waste a ton of plastic to stop my period, something which is completely unnecessary, since my body really shouldn't be wasting hormones making eggs, when I can't even legally have sex yet. I've also never ever spoken to my dad about my period; he's a great dad, and it really bothers me that I feel so uncomfortable sharing these kinds of things with him. A few months ago, I found some more eco-friendly pads I could use, I told my mum about them, and she told me to ask my dad to buy some. I still haven't asked him, even though I know he wouldn't be bothered. My mum asks him to buy tampons all the time.

I got my period in January. I had read somewhere that when periods first start, they may come and go for a few months, and February did come and go without a period, and I sort of convinced myself it would never come back. It did come back in March though, and after that it came back every month. It kind of makes it difficult when someone asks when my period started, because it basically started twice.

I told two friends, though with one it took me months to muster the courage, but with both the topic was never raised again. Can I also say I hate missing out on swimming when I have my period? Anyway, when I came back to school after lockdown, I found out a close friend of mine who I hadn't told about my period, actually had her period, and honestly, it helped a lot. Whenever one of us needed to change a pad, we wouldn't even have to say the words, and the other would know we needed to go to the bathroom, and I'm really grateful we can share the experience together.

The last things I have to say about my period are that I've had it for a year, but it still isn't regular, and I've had to throw away a lot of knickers as a consequence, and I don't know if I should be worried.

Also, I would never get my period at night, so I wouldn't wear a pad. But recently, I had it really bad, and the stain is still on the mattress, but wearing night pads doesn't help, because the main problem is when I sleep on my side and it all comes out that way, so I'm not sure what to do.

Written by Iulia

Every time I'm on my period, I always dread school. I find it hard to focus, to the point teachers tell me to "stop daydreaming". One of the worst things, I find, is having to make the seemingly endless journey to the toilets with a tampon concealed in my sleeve. It seemed as if all through sex education, the subject of periods was always met by people saying, "that's dirty" or else "ew".

I just wish we could talk about periods without a second thought about it being a "dirty subject". Lots of people have periods, so I think we should be able to speak about them and get the correct accommodation from establishments such as schools and workplaces, so we don't have to hide anything and so we can feel comfortable no matter what.

Written by Jasmine Bayley

Every word felt a little more,
Stomach churning, aching, raw.
Emotion twisting tight as a coil
Temper burning ready to boil.

Hunger grows and spots break out,
I want to scream; I want to shout.
Sadness, anger, love, and tears,
Must I go through this for all these years?

I don't mean to shout it's just what I do,
I don't mean to cry; I just feel so blue.
I just need a moment to sort out my head,
And cuddles and kisses and chocolate in bed.

Being a woman is no easy feat,
Some days I feel like I will be beat.
But the sun shines again, and the pain goes away,
although it will be back one day.
It's not all bad as it's only a few days,
It's part of me, one of nature's ways.

Written by Katie

Periods in Time

It began
Just before my ninth birthday –
Stomach cramps and blood.
Not just a trickle, but a flood.

I thought I would die,
But my mother –
As was her way –
Brushed my panic away
And made an appointment
With the local GP

Who drew a little diagram,
And explained –
In a clinical way –
What it all meant.

And so, it went.
Each month wrestling
With belts and clips
And bulky pads
That slid up my back
Whenever I sat.

I'm still haunted
By that day in school –
Red stained dress
And sticky rivulets
Trickling down to white socks

Period Power Charity

I saw it as a curse,
And it only got worse as I grew,
Debilitating pain
And days off work,
Curled up with hot compress,
Underwear and sheets a mess.

But over time, it became
The lifeblood
That nurtured three babies,
And it gave me
A kind of grudging respect.

And it came to be
That an early beginning
Meant an early end
And my body – up to its old tricks
Began menopause at thirty-six

A full-stop, an abrupt end
To that nurturing flow
That I had come to know
As a painful but reliable friend

And in the end
I felt bereft –
A feeling of being left
Empty and barren,
My 'womanly duty' done.

But now,
A new stage has begun.
The pain and flow have ceased,
Leaving in their wake
The satisfaction of a job well done
And a feeling of contented peace.

Written by Colleen Moyne

This isn't a horror story. But it damn well was. It's a little long, but not as long as the ten years this story actually took to come to a conclusion.

My first period happened when I was 13. By the time I was 17, periods were ruining my life. So painful I would vomit, be unable to stand. I would sweat, shiver, and pass in and out of consciousness on the bathroom floor with my head in my Nana's lap. I took painkillers; I threw them up in minutes. I put heat patches on; I sweated them off. I was hot, cold. My joints felt like they were being pushed apart.

If you'd put a gun to my head, I wouldn't have gotten up because I would rather have been put out of misery. Extreme? Yeah. But when you feel that pain, if you've ever felt it, and there's nothing you can do to stop it, time after time, dreading it, waiting for it, living on edge that at the drop of a hat, this would be the next 12 hours of my life...you'll probably do the same. There wasn't a spare cell in my body that wasn't on fire and being torn apart.

I couldn't stand up. I got dizzy and fainted. The pain – I couldn't speak, couldn't scream loudly, because doing that makes your belly contract and that was more pain. Just groan and grit my teeth and squeeze my eyes shut and wedge a towel between my knees and ankles to stop the joints from touching and catch the extra blood that wouldn't have been out of place on a murder scene. That time I was with my mum, at home, in comfort and safety. I wasn't in a stinking portaloo working as a farmhand with a load of 30 something blokes. I didn't have a towel then. I ruined a t-shirt instead. My hobbies were outdoorsy. I rode motorbikes, horses. I'd joined the army cadets. I liked shooting, fishing. Male based environments. At 17, I didn't have the emotional strength to show them my vulnerability, to deal with their misinformed opinions and reactions. I wanted to live my life, but the fear of being rendered incapacitated amongst a group of boys or men... I was not comfortable with that. It happened at a rally once. I was with my dad, helping my uncle and cousin do checks before the next stage of the race. In a crowd of 100, I saw perhaps 2 other women. Who could I talk to? Who was I supposed to ask? What was I meant to do? People thought then, and still think of having a period as like peeing. Somehow if it goes wrong and you can't control it, it's like you've peed yourself in public. Except, only 50 percent of the public will get it. 25 percent might understand... way less than that will help you. They think you're faking, somehow. Or stupid for not being prepared.

Because, if it wasn't clear, there was no warning. No predictability. Sometimes 3 months apart, sometimes twice in one month. I lived on the edge of my seat, in case of the bloodstains, you know? Boy scout style. I was always as prepared as I could be extra shirts, an ammo case of tampons (if I could change them safely), a whole pack of pads (if I could dispose of them properly), minty air freshener for the smell, antiperspirant to put on my face to stop it sweating, lipstick to hide the lack of colour, a back belt to hold me upright when the pain would bend me double before it took me to my knees. There's a lot of stuff to take on a date.

I didn't want to go to gigs, go on dates, nights out, holidays, sleepovers, play sports... what if this happened out of nowhere? What if I went on a date and passed out in the bathroom? What if I slept somewhere else and covered someone else's bedsheets in blood? What if I was sat on a plane, trapped amongst strangers, with one tiny bathroom when I felt that first murky gut-punch of pain? What if I moved and was covered in blood? No clothes to change into? That stink of dying blood hanging off me.

As you can see, I did not embrace womanhood. I did not enjoy my 'working body'.

I hated everything to do with menstruating.

Hated not being in control.

Hated not having my life.

Hated the embarrassment.

Hated the fear.

Hated the fact I simply had to 'deal with it'.

God, how I hated that phrase.

At 19, the doctor put me on the pill. It made me worse; he didn't believe me. The next time, back on the bathroom floor, after spraining my mum's hand from clenching it so hard, she called an ambulance. When she said it was menstrual, the call operator told her that they wouldn't dispatch an ambulance for that, that ambulances were for life-threatening situations and not to waste time.

My mum shouted, "I've been a woman all my life; I've raised three daughters to adulthood!" She knew what normal menstruation was and this wasn't it. "Do you want me to video this?" she asked. She told them I was so unwell I couldn't stand or physically speak.

The call operator told her she was clearly exaggerating, that periods did not do that. He hung up. Mum threw her mobile on the floor. I threw up so hard I hit my head on the toilet and passed out. I remember her stroking my hair, quivering with anger, and muttering idiot, idiot, idiot, under her breath. Between waves of pain, I told her it wasn't fair to call me an idiot when I couldn't mount a defence. She smiled and laughed and cried and stroked my hair some more.

One time, when I was 20, I crashed my motorbike trying to get home before the pain got too strong, before I got too weak to manoeuvre the bike; I was trying not to pass out. I was trying to win the diarrhoea race too. I didn't tell my dad, who taught me how to ride and bought the bike for me for my graduation present. He's a good man and I don't think he would have said anything bad to me. But, he would have told me to stop riding if I couldn't ride. I could ride, though. He would have told me that accidents on bikes kill people. I couldn't face it. I told him someone bumped it in the car park.

I got weaker.

I fell off a horse I was riding one time because I went over a jump and on landing, a spear of pain went through me. I lost my balance and hit the ground and frightened the horse. My instructor said I wasn't ready to progress. I went back to no jump work. I was ready to progress though! He didn't change his mind when everyone saw there was blood on the saddle; a leather saddle, so it wouldn't come out either! He said I had to manage it better. No one stops Badminton or the Olympics for a period. Everyone saw. Everyone knew. I wanted the ground to swallow me whole.

I had a piggy bank specifically for sanitary products. Being violently ill was damned expensive. Using four or five heavy overnight tampons in a day, plus changing the heavy overnight maxi pad that went with it. I knew it wasn't common, to go through that many, to lose so much blood. But everyone is different, and I detested talking about it, so I didn't have anything to measure against. I taped cling film and a towel to my mattress at night and slept on my side, not daring to move for the blood. I wore all black, which hid any blood spots. Long tops and scarves to sit on to put layers between me and chairs. Smuggled things into the washing machine. Even in front of my mum, I didn't want her to know. I know now I should have spoken to someone, but at the time, it was too much for me. I was so private, *am* so private, that even sat here writing this makes me cringe. I've got that attitude from somewhere. I didn't create that attitude spontaneously.

Then the pain came with the period and didn't go away, at all. The period ended and I still hurt. Slower, lower, more of a flu-like ache than being gutted with a blunt spoon. I lost weight. I didn't mind that so much, I was lighter for the horses. I was always tired. I drank more tea and went to bed earlier. My belly started to bloat; I looked like I'd swallowed a watermelon whole! I looked 3 months pregnant. I had to undo my jeans. With the bloat, my heart rate would skyrocket. I'd sweat. Sitting down hurt. Moving hurt. Standing up hurt. Just gas. Obviously a bit of wind. I ate indigestion tablets by the fistful. Perhaps I had a bad diet? I stopped eating gluten just in case. I ate more vegetables just in case. I drank more water just in case. I stopped the caffeine just in case. I got weaker. Perhaps I was unfit? I started going to the gym.

At a BBQ, I felt the signs and in a desperate panic because I was having such a good time and didn't want to leave took a packet of paracetamol and ibuprofen to fend it off. They were like sweets to me by then. Obviously, it was too much. I had to drive home high. I told a friend about it. She shook her head and gave me a packet of codeine and a packet of tramadol. Opiate based painkillers.

For the first time in months, the pain floated away. I slept like an angel. But then I had used them all and the pain came back. In a way, it came back worse. It was a clear comparison to how bad it was and what it took to make me feel better. I browbeat the doctor into writing me a prescription; I reasoned, I argued, I pleaded, I cried – anything I could think of to have access to something that would make it Goddamn stop HURTING. He wasn't happy about it. He said it was "unreasonable to prescribe such strong medication for something like periods". He would only agree to codeine. I showed him the pain scale I'd printed so I could use something concrete to explain what my life was like to people. I pointed to 7, "my pain prevents me from doing most activities". I pointed to 8, "my pain makes talking and listening difficult". I pointed to 9, "I can barely talk or move because of the pain and cannot focus on anything but how to manage my pain". I pointed to 10, "insensible or losing consciousness due to pain". He frowned and said I would be in hospital if it was that bad. I said that I knew that; perhaps he could inform the ambulance services of the same thing.

He wrote the prescription.

I took 100, 30mg of codeine every month. Sometimes my friend would top me up with tramadol. For a while, I felt fantastic! With the pain gone, I was bouncing for joy and with excess energy. I went to the gym – worked on getting rid of the small but persistent gut. I still bloated, though. I ate more vegetables, less bread. Less sugar, more water. Still, I bloated. It was painful. Not as bad as everything else, but still, I couldn't press on my belly without a sharp inhale and a wince. It stuck out like I was 5 months pregnant no chance of that! But perspective; I was better than I was so that was enough. I was tough. I could cope.

The opiates began to catch up with me. The fog descended. The vague, zoned out sensation made doing a master's degree trickier. It made my job as a delivery driver an anxious and slightly frightening affair. With the months passing, the fog in my brain got thicker. What was I saying? Doing? Thinking? My brain was made of fluff and mud. I slept more. My skin went grey and flaky. Dig deeper. I told myself. A master's degree is tiring – push on.

Then it happened.

I'd felt ill all week. Very nauseated. Odd kind of back ache. Went to the doctor, who gave me some antibiotics for a urine infection. Later that night, my partner (by then of 1 year) took me on a date to the cinema. My belly hurt, hurt, hurt. It was the size of a watermelon. My pulse in my fingertips and my neck was beating fast. Sweat was trickling down the back of my neck. I stood up to go to the bathroom and something between my belly button and hips ripped. I felt something tear. I ran (or more honestly, hobbled to the bathroom as fast as I could, feeling bile rise in my throat from the pain. My vision tunnelled. I flung myself into the stall and suffered a hideous moment of indecision about which end was more important. I decided that vomit on the floor was better than the other! I gave a stifled scream, biting my fist, tears and sweat streaming from me. The lady in the stall next to me asked if I was alright.

I was not. This was the most 'not right' I had ever been. I asked her to fetch my partner. Eventually, I dared to stand up and inch my way into the main foyer. My knees shook. The initial pain had subsided, but I knew it would be back and I knew I had to act quickly. My partner saw me and took a literal step back in shock at how ill I looked. He told me after "you were white, beyond white, grey, transparent, your lips had faded off your face". Bad, but still normal. Don't fuss. Don't make a scene. It's bad, but I always get through, I told him.

He half carried, half dragged me back to the car. I whimpered at the jolt every step put through my body. We didn't make it. I collapsed in a dirty stairwell, speckled with blackened chewing gum at 11:00 PM. He wanted to call an ambulance. I told him to call Mum and Dad because an ambulance wouldn't come.

Mum and Dad came and the 3 of them scraped me off the floor and put me in the boot of the car because I couldn't hold my body upright. Every time we went over a pothole or accelerated or braked I wailed and yelped. I remember their faces as the streetlights illuminated the car interior every few seconds. They spoke to me, about me. I couldn't talk – I felt drugged by pain.

"It has been worse" Mum told my partner and my dad who had never seen me like this before, he only saw the recovery. Neither of the men in the car could believe what was happening. Once home, they lay me down on the living room floor. I ate my painkillers and waited for it to go away. Eventually it would get bored and leave me alone, I joked to myself.

It didn't.

At 2:00 PM the following day, all 3 of them decided to call an ambulance. I made them wait that long. "Someone else needs it more than me" I said. "It will get better. I always get better. It's been worse honestly. I can speak, which is a good sign". The paramedic arrived looked at me. Asked me if I could stand, "I'd really rather not" I said with a grin. He enjoyed my sense of humour, my family didn't. He tapped my belly with his fingers, and I yelled. He sent a needle of morphine into my backside and said, "I don't know what it is, and that's a good enough reason to get you to hospital".

At the hospital, I was flung into a scanner. Doctors swarmed all over me – blood tests, injections, drips, more scans, more belly tapping. I snapped at the second doctor who did it. Yes, thank you, we have all successfully established that doing that hurts. For 2 days I wasn't allowed to eat or drink anything. Had a lot of morphine though. My lungs filled with fluid. My skin was yellow, and I stunk of sweat. My gums and tongue went white like tripe. Mum and Dad seemed to age visibly as they sat quietly beside my bedside watching the doctor's flurry around me.

They then found an 8-centimetre tumour on one ovary. It was actually shrinking because it had been full of blood and had ruptured and taken a lot of blood out of my system and was pooling in my abdomen. That's what I had felt tear. That was why I couldn't get rid of my little gut – there was a goddamn cannonball in my belly! Mum and Dad didn't say word. My partner stared at the doctor, his face hovering between outrage and incredulity. Then the questions. Cancer? What would happen now? Cancer? Would I be alright? How long could it be in there? The doctor said it was hard to say, months at least.

That there is some indication of other smaller tumours ruptured and since healed. Can't be certain it's cancer but very treatable if it is. "So, these things were growing and busting open whenever they fancied?" I asked. The doctor said it was quite likely.

Well, it's no wonder I felt so spectacularly shit.

I got poked full of holes and a camera went looking for a clearer picture than the MRI scan. Not cancer. Phew.

Stage 4 endometriosis.

Throughout my abdomen, uterine tissue had been growing in places it shouldn't, sticking my organs together and to the inside of my abdominal cavity. It would move when I worked out, and tissue would tear, and I would get little internal bleeds. My body would try to heal, but scar tissue is sticky, and it would fuse together more securely. That's why I felt sick. That's why I bloated. That's why I was so tired. That's why it hurt so much. Oestrogen fuels it. That's why the pill made me worse.

I was in the hospital for 8 days. While this sank in, the doctors said there was no cure.

My friends came to visit me, but I was so weak I couldn't open the packet of flame-grilled McCoy's crisps they brought me – for the iron, they joked. Less humorously, the doctors put me on a course of iron tablets for 5 weeks. The usual course is 2. I was off work for 3 months recovering. I would fall asleep after eating 3 or 4 chips from the sheer effort of it. My partner took 3 weeks off work to look after me. He would escort me from bed to bathroom, to sofa, standing behind me, arms wrapped around me, while I held onto his forearms and shuffled from room to room.

We tried not to think about the 'no cure' part. Lucky it was a tumour and not a blood clot In my lung, in my heart, in my brain, because that can happen. Rare? Sure, but look at the mess my body was in. I was 24. About a year later, I had surgery which pulled all the stuck together bits of organs apart. The surgeon cleared away all the uterine tissue with a minuscule, buzzing razor.

It took another 6 weeks to recover from that.

All the while, the four of us talked and researched. There must be something, something to help. Something to do. No cure? Liars. We had an answer. A total hysterectomy. Take the whole sodding system out. I'd do it myself if I had to – I was done with this whole situation. An organ I'd never asked for, didn't want, didn't like had been destroying my life for years and now it had tried its best to kill me. Nearly did it too. We went back to the doctors.

"Think about your future", they said.

"I am" I replied.

"You'll want kids eventually", they said.

"I'll adopt."

"It's irreversible."

"That's the plan" I said.

"You'll need life-long medication."

"So do diabetics."

"You'll regret it" they said.

"Not as much as I regret not demanding to be taken more seriously when I was younger and putting my family through hell."

They turned to my partner (now of 3 years) and asked him "what do you think about this?"

It was hard to tell which one of us was more outraged by this question.

"I think I want my partner to be happy and healthy and pain-free and alive, you complete pillock".

My mind was blown. At 16, still a legal child, I could bring a child, an irreversible, life-altering child into the world without a single person's intervention for concern about my future, life, and health.

At 25, I could get married, drive, vote, get a tattoo, work full-time hours, buy a dog, leave the country, drink, have a mortgage, join the military, and die for my country, but I wasn't considered aware enough, far-seeing enough, self-possessed enough, secure in my own mind enough to be believed that I did NOT want to have children! Disgusting. Enraging.

The more I argued for myself, the more I explained that my own life was more valuable to me than any currently non-existing children, the more they refused to believe me. 'Too emotional to be making life-altering choices' Quote. My health was being placed secondary to the belief that I would one day want children. That I would be willing, despite being seriously ill, to live in pain and misery so that I could one day have children. If conceiving them and giving birth to them didn't kill me. My expressed wishes, articulate, clear, and made in sound mind wishes were rejected. Now it wasn't just a biological lack of control over my body, it was a medical and social one too.

The consultant decided to give me a hormone-freezing injection for 6 months, so I could see what it would be like to live as a 25-year-old with a biological age of 50. If that's what it takes to convince you.

In 6 months, I was changed. I put on a stone in weight, calories that normally would have been burnt fighting the pain and injuries in my body. I lifted weights. I got strong. My skin glowed. The opiate fog faded, and I felt like myself for the first time in years. I felt alive for the first time in years. A letter came. After reviewing my case, my files and several discussions with other doctors, my consultant had recommended me for a complete hysterectomy.

In the hospital gown the day of the surgery, the consultant looked at me and said 'this isn't a guarantee. If we miss a bit, a few cells of endometriosis, it could come back.'

'Well then, don't rush the job...'

5 puncture wounds and 3 hours later, I was alive and safe and on the way to being well. I'd take another 3 months to recover, but it would be my last recovery. I'm now 27. That hysterectomy was one of the best things that ever happened to me. But that's what it took to let me have my life.

Endometriosis affects 1 in 10 uterus-owners. If your periods are ruining your life, if they are getting in the way of you living how you want to live, you put your foot down. It's your body and your pain. No one on the face of this earth should be able to dictate to you what you can and cannot put up with in your own body.

You have the right to request a second medical opinion.

You have the right to see a doctor of your choice.

You have a right to control over your body.

You have a right to live your life.

Written by Alexander Parker-Carn

My emotions are in turmoil, my stomach is in pain.

My hormones are just everywhere, the kids think I'm insane.

One minute I am raging, the next I'm on my knees.

My family are avoiding me, they say I'm hard to please.

Tampons, towels, lil-lets, the choices are so many.
To buy the best is hard to do when counting every penny.

Paranoid, I draw a bath, the third I've had today.
Another paracetamol to take the pain away.

For a week I lose control, I feel like I'm possessed.
Emotional and angry, and sometimes so depressed.

I know I'm not the only one, most women feel this way.
So when I'm on my monthlies don't ask if I'm OK.

Written by Corinne Boden

The Dreaded Time of the Month

It's like a massacre. Nothing escapes a good drenching. It ruins my clothes, my bedding, and my knickers.

It turns my life upside down for over a week of every month. Makes me hate myself and feel so uncomfortable in my own skin.

I'm mostly angry with just being me.

Every month I want it to be the last.

It never is.

I go for a wee – blood flows so fast down my leg, it drips off my ankle and onto the grey tiles on my bathroom floor. I can't wipe myself fast enough to stop it. It kills my already excruciatingly painful back to bend down and clean it.

It wakes me up in the night. I'm often lying in a pool of it. It doesn't matter that I got up at 5am to change my super plus tampon, because by 7am, the tampon is so drenched, it falls out when I sit on the toilet. No need to look for the string.

I seem to be incontinent all the way through too. I can't always distinguish if the wet patch on my dark trousers is piss or blood.

I pass clots too. I know when they're on their way out because my cramps feel like someone has put their hands inside me; squeezing my womb – like you wring out a wet flannel.

All that mess from a teaspoon's worth.

Written by Andrea Burford

A period (of misery).

A normal bodily function, surely?
What are you complaining about?
You're not poorly!

Aching cramps, heavy breasts, and backache for
days,
Irritable in so many ways.

Why are you so moody?
Will you snap out of it?

Blanket on, cup of tea,
Snuggled up in my pit.

Hot sweats, cold feet; the worst is low mood.
Increased appetite but only for comfort food.

What's the matter with you?
What are you whingeing about?
Bloated, fatigued with another spot breakout.

Leave me alone if you know what's best.
Oh womanhood! How truly I'm blessed.

Written by Charlie Smith

By Jess, aged 15

A reflection on my menstruation experiences

Unfortunately, being a woman has its own kind of burden. The preconceived notions of women, being the nurturing caregivers dominates our patriarchy. Therefore, when it comes to respecting our bodies' natural phenomenon, society can't keep up. Personally, I loathe menstruating every month because I see it as a burden that I cannot control. In fact, throughout my life I've wished that I wasn't a woman due to being burdened with a menstrual cycle.

I vividly remember my mother introducing me subtly to the concept of vaginal bleeding after I had finished a normal day at primary school. For both of us, talking about menstruation coincides as a hugely normal conversation. Even today, we speak openly about the idea of menstruation. Furthermore, my mother always instilled the idea that menstruation is a hugely normal phenomenon engrained in every woman's life which resonates in my overall outlook on menstruation. However, I've also witnessed other female members of my family, so embarrassed to talk about sanitary products in front of me but not my mother, even though I am on the same side as them. And I did challenge this with my mother, as to why this individual wouldn't talk about this subject, out loud, in front of me, but never really got an answer.

"Menstruation blood is the only blood that is not born from violence. Yet it is the one that disgusts society the most." (Maia Schwartz) This quote hugely resonates with society's attitude towards menstruation. Furthermore, it is also blood that a price is paid for. We pay a price to control this bleeding, which shouldn't be the case. As a woman, it grieves me to know that menstruation is seen to be a subject of immense disgust and taboo in society. It pains me to know that there are women around the world who are not fortunate enough to have access to sanitary products. It saddens me to know that illiterate women have no idea what menstruation is. In addition, the idea that sanitary products broke headlines in the 21st century for becoming free is some higher income countries, disgusts me even more.

On the other hand, I do understand and coincide with women who are forced to think that menstruation is a subject of impurity and disgust. As a 'BAME' woman, I've been shunned on numerous occasions from doing certain things like praying and fasting because menstruation is seen to be a vessel of impurity. Moreover, women are also forbidden to speak openly about this because society has created an uncomfortable stigma towards this taboo. Not just menstruation, blood itself for 'BAME' individuals is a connotation of impurity and weakness which is forbidden to be shed in public.

In my early years, menstruation had the ability to hugely deprive me, emotionally and physically. I felt like I was dying because I would always be living in fear. A fear of leaking through my skirt at school, a fear of leaking through my clothes at home, a fear of leaking blood all over my pyjamas under my duvet. I lose a lot of blood compared to the average amount of blood loss for a woman on her period. As a result, when I am menstruating, my stamina is drained even further which I try to overcome by going head-to-head with my body. I resist the urge to digest and pump my body with paracetamol because I am stronger than this. By enduring the physical pain, I have empowered myself and seen immense long-term benefits for my body and wellbeing because I am not in as much pain as I used to be in.

Obviously, this pain threshold ranges depending on the pressures being exerted within the body, but I am now able to withstand the high threshold of pain that I couldn't once in my life.

It deeply saddens me that as women, we cannot openly talk about menstruation. I understand the idea that it is a hugely private experience. Not every woman is comfortable talking about this taboo and I would also not like to be airing my dirty laundry in public. However, this isn't about menstruation and that is why I felt entitled to speak strongly about this today. This is about societies' prejudices against women being seen as unequal beings. It is ultimately about being able to express our emotions and experiences without feeling suppressed by these societal prejudices.

Written by Madii Hussain

My First Period

I was in my last year at primary school (age 10) when the headteacher (a nun) came into class and requested I join her at the office. I wasn't sure what she wanted me for, so I was nervous as I walked with her down the corridor.

When she reached the office, I went to sit down, and she told me to stay standing and then passed me a white paper bag with something inside. As I opened the bag, she told me "Your mum has called me, and she found blood in your pants so wanted me to tell you you've started your period. In the bag are towels that you need to press onto your pants to stop you from making a mess. You should have told your mum before coming to school."

She told me to go to the toilets and then back to class. I had no idea what either the headteacher or my mum were talking about... I wasn't injured or hurting! I locked myself in a toilet cubicle and opened the paper bag I had been given, taking out the thick, long padded item. I didn't know what to do with it, so I shoved it into my coat pocket and went back to class.

When I got home that afternoon I showed my mum what I had been given, and she asked why it was screwed up in my pocket and not in my pants. I explained I didn't know what to do with it and that I hadn't cut myself and didn't understand what I'd been told. My mum flattened out the crumpled item, showed me the 'sticky bit' to stick to my underwear and told me I had to wear three or four a day for the next seven days while I had a period.

"What's a period?" I asked my mum.

"It's a sign you are a woman now and every month you will bleed and must keep yourself clean so men can't smell that you are on a period. Change your towel a few times a day and put used ones in a bag In the bin. I'll make sure there are always a stock of towels in the bathroom cupboard... now go and sort yourself out and I don't want to see a mess like that in your pants again."

At 10 years old, I was ashamed, confused, and embarrassed – worrying about cleanliness, smells and with no idea what was happening to my body. My mum didn't mention anything more about periods, and it took me months to talk to one of my friends, whose mum then sat both of us down and explained it to us.

I was in my 30's when I spoke to my mum about how upset the situation had made me feel... she replied, "At the time, you didn't need to know any more – just to protect your clothes. That's how I was instructed when I was younger, and it did me no harm."

When I became a mum, I changed the generational learning that I'd been victim to and spent time explaining about periods in a healthy way for years before she got her first period. When it happened, she was excited and happy to share the news!

Written by Vicki Gwynne

People who bleed

People can conceal secret time bombs,
Baring their teeth in a grin

When they erupt, the silence they corrupt,
Could not be further from a win

When it's our time, although we may whine,
And have no reason to sing,

These pesky little bombs,
Are the reason we become mums,
And I think that's a fabulous thing.

Written by Imogen

Periods are a pain; it is expensive to buy sanitary products every month.

Periods make me moody and mad.

Physical effects include bloating, back ache, and stomach cramps.

Things I crave are sweet desserts and chocolate.

Written by Kat

I started my periods aged 9 – so 31 years ago! Looking back, it was very young! It wasn't pleasant to be dealing with such a huge event at such a young age… I remember being embarrassed to ask my parents to buy sanitary towels, especially my dad! It's not something you can pop off and do independently at such a young age. As I was a little older I was grateful that everything appeared to be "working normally" and I looked forward to children one day.

They became particularly painful around age 12 and I often felt faint and exhausted from them; it actually led to me having quite a lot of time off high school poorly. This, with the feeling of never feeling clean, wasn't a nice combination – I spent most of my teen years taking Feminax (the only thing that seemed to work for the pain). I went on the pill aged 12 because of the pain. This led to me having migraines and blackouts, although the cause was never pinpointed to being on the pill, I suspected it was.

Periods went on to be not too bad after my first child, but after giving birth to my second child, they didn't return. I went for scans internally to be told in my early 20s, I had no follicles in my ovaries and probably wouldn't have any more children. I was devastated. My (now) husband and I had only just had our first child together. It was such an emotional and testing couple of years; that 'something' I had once hated for the pain and associated with having periods, I was now grieving for not having! It was really bizarre. I certainly felt less of a woman for not having them. I was very lucky that they eventually made a return, and I went on to have 5 more children. I am very blessed and thankful.

However, I am now 40 and my childbearing years are done, so willing the menopause to actually appear for real now. One breakthrough I did discover whilst being a tester for PeriodPower was the Mooncup – I have never looked back. It gets rid of the "dirty" feeling associated with menstruation and also helps with pain and certainly assists with costs! I also use the washable sanitary towels just in case of small leaks but certainly feel much more confident working 13 hour shifts with the leakage chance a lot less than just with sanitary towels alone. The only small negative is it's a little awkward to use a Mooncup in a public toilet, I suppose wipes would have to be used. Also having a tilted womb makes it a little trickier, but not impossible.

I am glad I have found a good cost-effective combination to keep me feeling as clean and fresh as possible. It can be very expensive with 3 of us needing sanitary towels in the house. One of my daughters has regular bleeding pretty much constantly (they can't figure out why) so that can soon run up costs very quickly. Being a young adult, she prefers tampax and they are not cheap!

Looking to improvements – when I started high school/ left primary, we were given a little book that talked about periods and adolescents, along with a sample pack – that was probably one of the most useful things anyone has ever given me! What a shame they don't make them anymore. I think simplicity or Dr Whites wrote it, but it was a great informative and useful resource; particularly when young girls have nobody to ask or actually don't have the confidence to speak to someone about it. Imagine a 9-year-old girl who doesn't have a mum, or anyone other than males. I vividly remember how hard it was to talk to my dad to ask him to buy pads. I think I actually had tissue in my knickers for about 3 hours until I managed to steal one of my mum's sanitary towels. Please let's not carry this feeling on of girls and women being afraid to ask.

Written by Surina Ainsworth

Secondary School 1972

The newness of everything kept us in our place at first. However, as the months went by we became bolder. As soon as one teacher left the classroom to go to another room, we talked instead of brushing up on the lesson for the next class, like we had done at first. The breaks between classes became chatty affairs, but never with enough time to say what we wanted. So, instead of sitting cowed or in awe of the teacher, we talked behind our hands or dropped something on the floor so we could turn around and talk to the girl behind.

There was so much to talk about, like the films we had seen or trashing out the merits of *Lovely Leitrim* versus the Beatles' *Day Tripper*. Frank Sinatra's songs, like *Strangers in the Night,* were never talked about because the old people liked him so he couldn't be hip. Even the most important news had to be doled out because time was scarce. The time Úna was dying, it took her the whole morning to tell us. Getting the details of her sickness was more nerve-racking than the Saturday matinee film sequels we saw in the Odeon, where every week the good guy was in terrible danger. We'd have to wait until the following Saturday to see if the train would run over his body tied on the tracks or if he would manage not to fall to his death below, as he clung onto the cliff edge by his fingertips. Úna did her best to take us out of our suspense about the fatal sickness, but only managed to tell us in snatches; it wasn't until the yard break that we learned the whole story.

We heard the first part on *An Lár,* where we met every morning to walk to school together. When she saw me and Kait waiting, she rushed over saying she had something very important to tell us, but she couldn't start until Evelyn arrived, which she did after what seemed like ages. We gathered close around Úna as we walked to school while she told us the story of how she was dying.

"Yesterday evening, about the time the Angelus was ringing, I felt a tickling between my legs." Us three looked at her wondering what that had to do with dying.

"Why didn't you check to see what it was?" Ev asked as we thought there was no big deal about being itchy.

"I was at study, like ye were, so I couldn't. Janey Macs the itch was driving me crazy."

"Maybe you wet yourself?" Kait said and we stopped and smiled at Úna to let her know that even if she had, we were still her friends.

"I was thinking that too and that the wee was trickling down and causing the wet feeling between my legs."

"It would be terrible if you did wet yourself."

"I know, so that is why I said to Sr Beatriz, "*An bhfuil cead agam dul amach?*""

"That was the best thing to do." By now we had reached the classroom and she continued telling us in a low voice.

"Well, as soon as I got inside the toilet, I bolted the door so no one could walk in on me. Then I touched my gigeen," Úna said.

"You didn't!" Evelyn roared in shock, without realising she was shouting. Sister Agata was down at our desk.

"An bfhuil siad ag caint?"

"Nílimid," we all said at the same time, but the nun stayed standing by our desk and because of that, it wasn't until the break that we heard the full story.

On the way down the stairs Evelyn said, "I betchya there was an earwig stuck in her knickers and that was what was causing the itch."

Sometimes when our mammies took in the washing from the line, there would be an earwig among the clothes, but Kait had a different idea.

"Twasn't. It was a hair, so it was," she said blushing. Me and Evelyn looked at her wondering why she had gone so red.

"What would a rib of hair be doing down there?" I asked in a mocking tone, not believing Kait could be such a silly goose thinking a rib of hair could fall into your knickers.

Kait got even redder and said in a low voice, "Cos they grow around your gigeen too."

"They don't," I said but Úna who was walking slowly behind us nodded her head, agreeing with Kait.

"You're codding! Hair only grows on your head, you silly goose."

Úna told me to shut up because what had happened to her was important and we had to know about it. Sitting on her haunches and us huddling around her in a corner of the yard, she whispered the rest of the story wanting only us to know and no one else, not even Nuala McCabe who had started to sort of hang around with us.

"When I took my hand away, the tips of my fingers were red with blood. I washed them but I was shaking with fright thinking all the blood in my body was spilling out through my gigeen."

"You poor thing," Kait said. "What did you do?"

"I went back to the study hall. Sr Beatriz was sitting on the high podium in the middle where she watches us study."

"Did ya tell her?"

"I didn't. Just said I didn't feel well and was going home."

"But you were bleeding."

"I know I was, but my heart was in my mouth thinking, I was going to die. I wanted to see Mammy before I died, so that's why I left and didn't tell the nun."

"You were right. Did your mother send for the doctor?" Ev asked.

'She didn't. She gave me a clatter across the head and told me to keep quiet in front of the small ones when I started screaming. 'Mammy, Mammy, I'm going to die! There's blood coming out of me!"

"A clatter?" we all asked at once, this piece of the story being more surprising that what happens at the Matinee.

Úna shushed us by saying, "Yeah, a clatter." Then she continued. "She told me..."

"Why did she give you a clatter?" Ev insisted. She was still puzzled as to why any mother would hit you if you were dying.

"Because for some reason or other she was really cross and said to me. 'Get into that room there and wait until I am finished washing the spuds and have them on to boil, then I'll deal with you.'"

Being told to go into the room was making Úna go out of her mind with worry because when any of the family were sick enough for the doctor to come, they were put into the downstairs bedroom to wait for him. She was in the sick room but at the same time she thought she couldn't be very bad if her mother had given her a wallop. Úna waited, biting her nails until the door was pushed open and her mother told Úna what was wrong with her.

"What did she say?" Kait asked and we all gathered closer to Úna to hear if our friend was dying.

"That I was a woman."

"A woman? You're a girl," Ev said disappointed with that piece of news.

"She said I was a woman now and I had to be careful not to go too near a man."

"Not to stain him with the blood, is it?" I asked, thinking it had to be that but wanted to be sure.

"I don't know but she said the blood was normal and all women get it."

"I don't want to be a woman," I wailed

"When you grow more, you'll be one too whether you like it or not."

"I won't" I insisted.

"Shut up, Arlene. Let Úna finish or we'll all be dead before we hear the rest of what happened."

"Mam gave me a piece of a thick towel and told me to put it into my knickers. She said when she had money she would buy a belt thing to hold the towel thing up."

"A belt?" I said, thinking of the belts Daddy wears around his trousers and the ones Mammy has for her dresses which had buckles.

Kait asked, "A big towel?"

"No, small like a face towel but it had loops at each end."

"Will you have blood every day?"

"No, Mam said it would stop after a few days but come back every now and then."

"Are you wearing the towel now?"

"Ya, that's why I'm walking slow, so it won't fall off."

"Is it full of blood."

"No, there's only a spot or two. Mam gave me an auld towel that's no use and showed me how to make pads from it."

"Pads?" We all echoed in a surprised tone.

"Ya, to fit between my legs."

"Did you make any?"

"I made three last night, because Mammy said I have to change them every day and soak them in cold water, so they are easier to wash."

"Wash the blood out, you mean?"

"Ya and I have to put the basin in the coal house."

"Why in the coal house?"

"So the young ones won't see them and ask questions."

For the next few weeks, we spent every free minute wondering why girls bleed and became women. Bleeding and sanitary towels was the theme of our conversation when we'd meet in *An Lár* at break, as well as before and after study periods.

Did old women bleed too?

Did boys and men know girls bleed?

If you didn't stop bleeding, would you die?

We wondered about all these questions and also wondered if nuns, who spoke like women but didn't have hair, had periods?

Talking so much about blood coming out of the gigeen made us remember what Kait had said about hair growing on her gigeen. We wondered if she had told us the truth or was it just a story. Me and Ev asked her if it was really true hair grew on her gigeen.

"It does, so it does," she said and got red.

"I don't believe you. Come on, show us."

Kait got redder than the heart on the Sacred Heart. Her face bursting into flames was normal for us, so we kept on asking even though she was nearly on fire.

"Oh, shut up you two! Janey Macs, yer worse than Baby Patrick. Here, I'll show you mine," Úna said. It was ginger like the hair on her head. It stunned us into silence, although later we wondered if you had to comb it every morning for school.

Then at the beginning of second year, as though to teach me a lesson for not believing Kait, black hair started to grow under my armpits and around my gigeen.

The other two got their periods short after Úna's. Mine didn't come until a few months later. I wasn't frightened like Úna had been but at the same time I didn't tell Mammy I knew about periods because she would give me a lecture about 'nice girls not talking about certain things.' So, I said "Mammy, I'm bleeding. Will we go to Dr Kelly to see if I'm sick?"

"No Mary. What is happening to you is that you are becoming a woman."

"A woman?"

"Yes, and it is important you say three Hail Marys night and morning for holy purity."

"Will holy purity stop the bleeding?"

"Mary! Don't be impertinent. Nice girls must be pure so if you say your prayers, Our Lady will keep you safe."

"Alright, Mammy," was all I said but I saw she was better than Úna's mammy because she bought sanitary towels in the chemist for me. They were twelve pads of cotton wool inside gauzy material in a plastic bag. Mammy told me if I ever had to buy them myself, I had to wait until there was no man about to ask for them. She also said to wrap them in newspaper when I took them off. It was important they were hidden at the bottom of the rubbish bin, so no one would see them.

"Mammy, if everyone gets periods why do we have to be ashamed of them?"

"Mary, it's vulgar to talk about certain things. Modesty is a virtue and I want you to behave like a nice girl. Do you hear me?"

"A course I do," I said and walked out the door before she could say more.

This is an excerpt taken from my book, "The Figure in the Graveyard"

Written by Honor Harlow

It's a curse

It's that time of the month, wating for the monthly visitor.

A visit from Aunt Flo, she'll bring The Red Baron and Bloody Mary~ maybe Carrie will join us too, she's riding the cotton pony.

During the Moon time we'll deal with the Lady Business~ Girl flu! I'll earn the Red badge of courage. Mother Nature's gift?

The Crimson Tide comes in shark week~ Code Red!

I'm having the painters in, the colour's Red wedding, look at the blob on the rag.

I'm checking into the red roof inn~ just for a few days.

Written by Jenny Ermoyenous

"After years of not swimming on holiday and PMS induced nausea, I really started to resent my period. As I got older, I began to appreciate it so much more. For me it symbolises the beautiful gift of creating new life. Although it can give me mood swings and painful cramps, my period is a significant part of me that I wouldn't change for the world."

I think this book idea is great and will educate so many!

Written by Nicole Morrison

Menstruation

The first spots of blood, but what does it mean?
Bother, already, ibuprofen calls,
Embarrassed, white trousers, can it be seen?
Excitement, an adult, grown up at last,
Dilemma, off shopping, tampax or food?
Relax, not pregnant, won't have to tell Mum,
Panic, am I dying? No, but they'll marry me now,
Relief, he won't call me, safe for a while,
Resignation, rejected, a hut on my own,
Disgust, the wrong body, it's winning again,
Despair, a failure, never to be Mum,
Grief, new life lost, what did I do,
The first spots of blood, what else does it mean?

Written by Becky Parker

'Perfect Periods' They Said

The first time anyone who menstruates starts their period is always memorable. I always thought that it would be a 'spot' or a 'circle' like everyone says it is. It was not. August 2017, 12-year-old me, was happily sitting on my parents' bed. The sun rays beaming through the windows with two builders in our one and only bathroom. What I presumed would be an ordinary day of doing sequin art did not turn out like that. I sneezed. That was when I felt it. A rush of adrenaline with a large pinch of nervousness spread all over my body. What just happened? Due to the builders, I was not able to go into the bathroom to check. I do not remember how long I waited for them to go out onto the porch for a break, but I immediately went inside and realised it was more than a perfect large circular spot.

It seemed pretty exciting. I was finally a young adult! That euphoria ended quickly when I started getting cramps and headaches. It was definitely much more painful than I was told it would be and I was not prepared. Since then, every time I have had my period, I have always gotten cramps. Whether I am at school or at home, my periods do not seem like they want to cooperate with me. They want to come and go whenever they want without any warning.

After my first few periods, what I quickly realised was that your friends are your best supporters when you are on your period. Sunday 14th February, Valentine's Day. The day that I thought I was going to relax and just treat myself at home. Like they say though, go with the flow. My periods decided to take it quite *literally* that day. This was the worst time I have ever had them. I sat on my sofa for endless hours, underneath the duvet with my cramps becoming increasingly painful, to the point where I could not feel the contractions. I was dying on the inside, thanking God that it was not a school day. I felt terrible. I had only wanted to relax. Why could my periods not start on the 15th instead? What made my day better was when a friend of mine rang my doorbell to drop off some doughnuts for me! Exactly, what I was craving for!

The physical effects do not only affect me when I am resting. Physical education and swimming are definitely when I hate getting my period. Swimming, yes; I can wear a tampon, but going in the water when I have painful cramps? Pass. The worst is when even if I do not go into the pool with cramps and I start doing butterfly stroke; I can feel the cramps slowly creeping back. Some people have said to me that running around and doing exercise should help with the flow but that is not always the case. Especially when it comes to gymnastics and hurdles. Unbearable.

If periods, as a 15-year-old girl, can affect me so badly on one day when I was not working or even in simple daily activities, it would definitely impact my job in the future. Would it not? This makes me think sometimes: do I want a job where 'Period Leaves' are acknowledged or not? If my period pain continues the way they are now, I might need to sometimes take a day off. But that does not mean I accept I become weaker in any sort of way when I menstruate. It means I want employers to understand the effects that periods have on people who menstruate. If I were to take sick leave, it would imply periods are an illness- which is highly inaccurate. You exist because of the menstrual cycle, yet we have chosen to make it a sickness. In some schools, menstrual supplies are not self-accessible, demonstrating silently the stigma surrounding periods.

However, periods are just not about the physical effects- it affects us mentally as well. Sometimes, I get really emotional when I menstruate. I lose control over everything – my tears, my anger, my joy, and my sadness. A movie scene that I have watched before will just seem more emotionally powerful than ever before. Let us be honest, we have all blamed the menstrual cycle at least once for our emotions and the things we do (or avoid to do).

There is so much more to periods than just the effects of them. The products available to us also make a difference. Firstly, sanitary towels need a new name. The word 'sanitary' implies periods are 'dirty' hence need something to 'clean it up'. This is not the case. However, these pads are adult nappies. You are lying if you have never thought you are essentially wearing a diaper. Due to these pads, I never feel comfortable wearing tight clothing such as leggings and prefer loose joggers instead. I understand why many people do not wear tampons even though I was quite scared to wear one for the first time. Despite everyone saying, 'you cannot lose the string' it still scared me. It made no sense to me how a string could not just snap off. If you are clumsy like me you lose things bigger than a string all the time- locker keys, pens and the list never ends. How could someone tell me this? Fun fact: I did not lose it and that was quite a relief for me. The not so fun fact: it is much harder to use than it looks. There is a certain angle, you have to be relaxed and there are so many ways to put it in! Every time I did it, my mum was sitting outside the door waiting for me to say, 'Yes I finally did it correctly!' but instead had to hear about 10 times 'Yep. I definitely did it wrong'. I did not even feel like I was trying to wear a tampon. Instead, I felt like I was reading a physics question which made me think – 'when did we learn this?' and hopelessly trying a hundred ways to figure out the answer. Eventually, I did get there in the end and the one thing I learnt is that it does truly take practice.

Pads and tampons are not the only options accessible though. We must raise awareness of the varied menstrual supplies available. I have never tried period pants, menstrual discs, menstrual cups, or even reusable pads which I agree are better for the environment without doubt. The first few years when I was being taught about periods, no one really told me that reusable ones existed! We need to educate more in schools about reusable products from the same day young children are taught about pads and tampons. Not later. From what I have seen on TV, they are hardly advertised in comparison to the infamous blue liquid poured on pads. It was mainly being taught about disposable tampons and pads. This needs to be changed.

Why do I not use reusable products? My periods are so heavy that there is always that continuous fear of leaking despite using disposable supplies and not being able to find a place to change, which is always at the back of my mind. No matter how brave you are about not trying to cover your stains, there will always be people who judge you negatively, with disgust, and I am not ready for strangers on the street to come up and tell me 'I have a little something'. In the near future, I think I might start trying reusable products and see if it is suitable for me because I admit, the amount of plastic used to make these disposable products is nonsensical.

Have you ever gone shopping for period products? When I stood in front of all the products I could purchase for the first time, it just hit me that there are so many. I thought it was simple: wings, no wings, light, heavy, night. I was wrong. There are so many to choose from that honestly sometimes I don't even know the difference between some of them – they just look the same and at the end of the day they all have the same function.

This lack of education stems from the taboo around menstruation. The code words I have used before periods include traffic light, Japan, code red and monthlies. Now that I have grown up and reflect on this, I do not understand why in the first place I used these words. Periods are not a disease; it is natural and out of my control. In fact, a survey which I conducted in February 2021 showed that 23.9% of 284 people did not feel comfortable discussing periods including those in Year 7, 8, 9, 10, 11, Sixth Form, and staff at my school. How is this acceptable? Both people who menstruate and people who do not menstruate should all feel comfortable. Some of us may not feel comfortable because as young children we were told to keep it discreet. That we were impure. That it is only a girl's thing.

Yet, the main change we need to bring, is to remind people that periods are not those "one off" events. For some people it might happen a couple of times a year, but for others every month. The symptoms that each person who menstruates gets differ to everyone and they cannot help it. It is not a choice. These symptoms can change over the years, worsen, or even get better. But essentially, it becomes a life-long thing. Perimenopause symptoms appear, then menopause symptoms. It's an emotional and physical challenge that people who menstruate take on for years. Some will not even complain the slightest bit and keep working silently as if nothing is happening on the inside- pretending it doesn't even exist.

1) Numerous days of physical and mental suffering in silence
2) Numerous days of headaches
3) Numerous days of an aching body

4) Numerous days of cravings
5) Numerous days of avoiding daily activities such as household chores
6) Numerous days of not swimming
7) Numerous days of sadness
8) Numerous days of embarrassment
9) Numerous days of pretence
10) Numerous days of lacking motivation
11) Numerous days of questioning yourself
12) Numerous days of not being understood by others
13) Numerous days of spoiling clothing in public places
14) Numerous days of figuring out where to change menstrual supplies
15) Numerous days of trying to fit that extra period product in your pocket
16) Numerous days of consistently checking for leakages
17) Numerous days of waking up to stained bedsheets
18) Numerous days of hiding stains
19) Numerous days of earning money to buy menstrual supplies
20) Numerous days of spending savings on menstrual supplies
21) Numerous days of spending savings on painkillers
22) Numerous days of heating up a hot water bottle
23) Numerous days of missing school/work
24) Numerous days of waiting for change

This is just a small part of what happens to people who menstruate during their lifetime.

We want to make a change. To make sure no one feels embarrassed because they cannot afford menstrual supplies.

All Things Periods

To make sure everyone has what they need – not just the bare minimum. To make sure no one thinks periods are a weakness.

They are a superpower.

Written by a student at Northwood College for Girls

Menstruation Sensation

A series of short satirical poems about period products

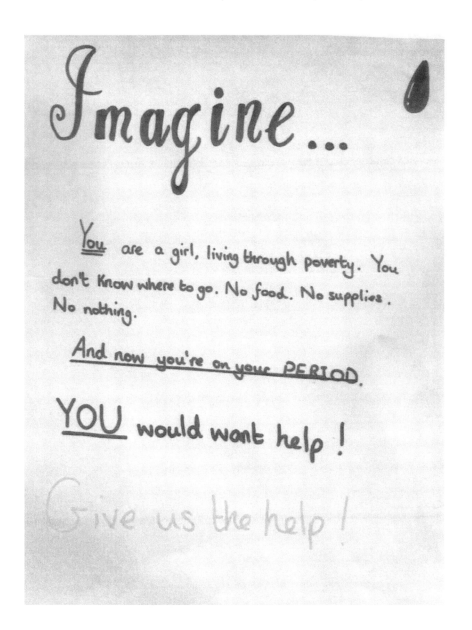

Menstrual Cup

Moon Cup, oh moon cup!

Hey what's up?

What's it like to collect all this blood?

Aren't you fed up with this heavy flood?

What's it like to carry something so full of shame?

For every problem menstruating women are to blame

Blood from gun shots and knife attacks is okay

But blood from a woman's uterus, no way.

How come people accuse you of stealing a girl's virginity?

When only a man's penis can decide over a woman's dignity

At least you're good for the environment that should pay your dues

Dumb bleeding woman here, climate change is obviously just fake news

Written by Anja Summermatter

A Serenade for a tampon

You most luxurious creation of cotton
How could your services ever be forgotten?
You bring our comfort to the max
This is why we need to pay tax
To insert you feels better than eating cake
(Which isn't taxed by the way, it's essential so they say)
My cravings for you keep me at night awake
You are such a luxury we need to keep you hidden
So all these poor men are not shame ridden.

Written by Anja Summermatter

Pads

Not quite an iPad, my pad
It's more like a diaper, my bad
That's what the girls use who are not so cool
It's unhygienic who can you fool!
A blood-soaked pad causes big uproar
Than the rapists they can continue to ignore
Blame it all on Eve and the original sin
As a woman there's no way you can win

Written by Anja Summermatter

Marilyn Menorrhea

Menstruation
Menorrhea
Periods
Bleeding
It's that time of the month

Shame
A secret,
Be discreet about it.

Blame,
A punishment,
Don't complain about it.

Fame,
No Mercy,
Don't speak about it.

No one speaks about blood on Marilyn's white dress
I wish Marilyn knew she wasn't a mess.

Pre-menstrual syndrome
PMS
PMT
PMDD
That's when they are crazy

Madness,
On some days,
I wish I could tear the house down.

Period Power Charity

Sadness,
On other days,
I wish I could jump of the balcony.

Gladness,
That one day,
I wish I could make it come earlier.

No one speaks about how Marilyn's life was rough
I wish Marilyn knew she has always been enough.

Menstrual Cramps
Dysmenorrhea
Period Pain
Belly Cramps
Aren't they exaggerating?

Aggravation,
Every hour,
The pain is agonising.

Desperation
Every minute,
The pain is unbearable

Contemplation
Everyday
This pain is suicidal.

Everyone treated Marilyn like a trophy on a shelf
I wish Marilyn knew how to love herself.

Written by Anja Summermatter

Endo Waves

How come my brain knows
how much this hurts
and yet it is surprised every month
when the waves throw me off again.
As if I needed to forget about it to live
before I'm there again
wishing I could drown myself in that ocean…

Written by Anja Summermatter

By Anonymous

My Period Writing

Periods. Blood. When you say blood to a man, his mind will probably go to violence. Getting shot, an action film, the trending video game. The word Is often associated with injury, the blood leaving the body through an opening that isn't meant to be there, something going wrong. For girls, the word had a completely different meaning. The "time of the month" or "bloody Mary". Her period. A regular occurrence for most women, and one that we dread every month. The dread can come in many forms, for me, it is the inevitable, menstrual cramps that come at some point during day two and often don't ease off until, at the earliest, the end of day three, often carrying on into day four. Then there's the constant craving for chocolate, which annoyingly comes with a nausea that forbids me from even smelling something sweet. However, for other women, it can be a time of grief as well. The appearance of a period when a woman is trying for a baby must feel like an awful loss. I won't pretend to know the feeling. But when wishing for a baby, your period must feel like a curse.

One thing that has always humoured me about blood is the gender differences. I remember a boy cutting himself at primary school once and not liking the look of the blood dripping off his arm, his friends told him to stop being such a girl, "it's only a bit of blood". I didn't think anything of it at the time but looking back it frustrates me. The insinuation that all girls have such a strong dislike of blood. In reality, that's hardly an option when it is all we see for one week a month.

There was a trend online recently of girls talking to boys about their period and filming how much they know. One guy thought that a pad stuck to your labia rather than the pants, with a little hole in it so you could go to the loo. Another thought that her period was only a couple of days long, and that a single tampon was all she needed to stop the flow over those days. It boils my blood (excuse the pun) to think that people can really be this clueless. But I'm not angry at them, more at the situation. There aren't that many boys that would go out of their way to research periods and if that's the only way they're going to learn, then the likelihood is that they just won't. I learnt more about my period watching entertainment on telly than I did as a child in school.

When we did sex education in primary school, I got so angry when they separated the boys and the girls. I didn't understand why they had to and why we couldn't learn about the same things. Even so, the video informing us about our periods was next to useless. It focused on biology. Ironically, I learned more about my period in Year 7 science when we learned about reproduction. That's the issue though; schools don't teach us what we need to know about our periods, and it certainly needs to teach males more. After all, if it wasn't for a woman's period (or lack of) they wouldn't even be here. No one would. Another gender difference I suppose would be art. In art at the start of school we learnt about a man that collected his blood over the course of a year and filled a sculpture with it. The whole class wondered at such an interesting statement. I loved it as I've always had a fancy for the slightly morbid. Comparatively, I researched an artist for my A-level who collected her period blood and painted with it. I loved it and found her work so beautiful and interesting, however many people in my class were more horrified by the thought. I wonder how differently they would have reacted if I had used the male's work instead.

A couple of years into secondary school a classmate asked one of our teachers to go to the toilet. A simple request that he agreed to. When she picked up her bag most girls understood that maybe she didn't just need to use the toilet. However, our teacher (a male) stopped her at the door and asked if she needed to take her bag with her. She said she did, but he refused to believe her or understand the situation. She had to stand by the door in front of everyone and inform him that she was currently bleeding so needed her bag for her sanitary products. Once he had realised, our teacher got embarrassed and let her go. This would probably not happen with a female teacher as she would understand straight away because she probably goes through the same thing. Though again, I don't believe that it was wholly our teacher's fault. This incident did have a lot to do with a lack of education. Teachers should know about these things especially as it is something that will always affect the girls in their class.

Many of the female teachers in school keep a pack of period products in their desk or bag because they know that so many girls will come to them in an emergency need for products. Teachers should not be needing to spend their money buying things for students that should be available for free. When I realised that so many teachers had to do this, not just in my school but everywhere, I decided to do something about it. I set up dignity boxes in my school's toilets. These are simply little boxes full of sanitary products. It means that if a girl comes on unexpectedly or doesn't have enough products, she can take some without the indignity of having to ask someone for help. It also means that she can take some for her family if she knows that they don't have any or if she may need some for over the weekend or evenings. I know that these boxes are being used regularly and are even reported to improve school attendance. This is such a simple thing but makes such a big difference. If all public toilets had them it could help people and families, and potentially improve people's lives massively.

I have always believed that period products should be free. Until recently they were deemed as luxury items for taxation purposes, they still are in some places. Of course, condoms and shaving products are seen as necessities. Hospitals provided free shaving products to the men there, but no free sanitary products to the women. How is that fair? To think that if you are on your period in a hospital, someone has to go out and buy sanitary products for you, but if a man wants to shave, "nah not a problem, here have a free razor". An example of gross gender divide. I'm of the opinion that if men had periods too, many of these problems would disappear, maybe we'd even have gender equality. I believe that the fact that women have periods have allowed men to put themselves above us for centuries. Especially when people believed that having a period meant that a woman was possessed by Satan. Alas, I don't think even Satan would wish this on us.

In some cultures, women are still shunned and physically isolated whilst they menstruate. Some Christian churches don't allow women to attend services whilst menstruating or within days of childbirth.

Another issue that concerns me is the plastic and chemicals in menstrual products. Did you know that 90% of an average sanitary product is plastic? That's roughly 4 carrier bags worth of plastic in just one pad or tampon. To top it off, in the UK alone, one truckload of sanitary products ends up in the ocean every year. That's not even counting all of the ones that end up in landfill and God knows where else. It horrifies me, and most women don't know. They don't know because periods aren't talked about. I started my period in year 7 and from day one I was using reusable products. I started using a moon cup on my second period and immediately took to it. Then under a year later, me and Mum discovered reusable pads. At that point we barely needed any disposable ones anymore. By then however, we were already using all natural, plastic free ones. Recently I discovered period pants, which are so useful. And of course, there are other, jam sponges, ziggy cups (which can be used during sex), and simply biodegradable pads and tampons. If all women used reusable products of one kind or another, the plastic waste in the country would massively reduce. I know that not every woman would feel comfortable with it, and probably many just don't care. But there are so many that would switch if they only knew that these products existed. I pushed to raise awareness of these in my school as well. There are now posters in the girls' toilets describing how these products work.

I hope that gender equality will exist one day. That we will be able to talk about our bodies without being shamed or shutdown, that the existing taboos will be a thing of the past. For now, though, I will settle for raising as much awareness as I can and hoping that others will listen and do the same.

Written by Gigi Ermoyenous

When I was 13, I went to stay at my dad's house the weekend when I got my period. I hadn't had my period very many times before and was completely unprepared to find blood running down my legs and not a pad in sight! Far too embarrassed to tell anyone, I found some tampons of my step mums in a drawer. So many different sizes and colours, I was very intimidated. I picked out a small yellow one and opened up the little packet. I remember my mum telling me when I used them it had to go in at an angle – which angle it was, however, I wasn't sure. Fumbling around, I tried to insert it forward. Though it was so painful, I assumed when it hit a wall that the task was complete. 🌢🌢🌢

When we left to go out, I could hardly walk, but I tried to keep it together. When we got home my underwear was covered! I tried to take the tampon out, only it hurt so badly I thought I might have to go to the hospital! Nope – that was far too much of a humiliating prospect! I yanked the string as hard as I could until it felt like I was pulling out my guts! I managed to get it out, but I could hardly sit down all day and had to try and dry my underwear before layering up the loo role!

Moral of the story, always put your tampons in facing backwards. We shouldn't be embarrassed to ask for the right sanitary products, (most likely it will save more pain than it might cost us to ask).

Written by Millie Stere

My periods had always been a problem since I was 13. Painful, heavy, bloating, you name it, I had it! Even that lie that after having a baby your periods get lighter and less painful!

When I was told that I had to have a hysterectomy when I was 42 (took me from the age of 37 with arguing with male doctors) I cried with relief with the knowledge that I'd never have to have another period.

Written by Natalie Adams

I feel I'd been lucky with my periods, I started later than my younger sister and felt clued up at 14 when they did start. I had books about puberty that helped me get my head around it. I didn't like sanitary towels AT ALL and quickly moved to using tampons, which worked for me with light flows and only 3-day bleeds. Reading up on the environmental impact and totting up the costs, means I'm now stocked up on menstrual cups and pants instead.

I took my regular, light cycle for granted in my early-20s, not letting it stop me playing sports, going swimming, and having sex (that's allowed too you know!) But then a battle with anorexia in my late 20s meant I had one last period in April 2011 and little did I know that they'd not return until the end of 2017. I knew being ill would affect my menstrual cycle, and fertility. Thanks to recovery, and a balanced diet, I got my period back and was able to conceive our son, who was born in 2020. I don't take periods for granted now, we need to celebrate "the time of the month" and our bleeds.

Written by Sarah Robertson

Periods.

No two girls will ever be the same.

Except of course we all suffer the pain

Back ache, cramps, drowsiness

Feeling hot, nausea, the list goes on

My thoughts

Personally, I can get symptoms up to one week before I start. My blood pressure drops, I get back and stomach pain as well as soreness and hot flashes. It even goes to the extent of flu like symptoms!

Periods are often disregarded, and women often suffer in silence and do all the things men do (career) and more. It can often be a barrier, especially in physical activity and we are expected to suck it up and carry on

While some women don't experience major mood changes, hormones can cause our emotions to fluctuate e.g., cry easily and anger.

It is still a taboo which even other women do not support each other on.

Written by Mala

Safe, affordable, menstrual products are essential for anyone who menstruates. But around the world, millions of women, girls, and people who menstruate can't afford to buy or don't have reliable access to the safe menstrual products they need. Whilst regular access to sanitary products is crucial for women and girls, whether they're disposable or reusable, the use of conventional, disposable menstrual products is harming the environment.

Most sanitary products contain up to 90% plastic, while tampons have plastic applicators and sometimes come in individual plastic wrappers. The production of plastic and improper disposal of these products is filling up landfills, where they take years to biodegrade whilst releasing vast amounts of greenhouse gasses, causing air pollution and global warming.

Some menstrual products are also flushed down the toilet, which means that disposable pads and tampons can end up in our seas and washed up on our beaches. This has a detrimental effect on humans, the wildlife, and natural habitats.

Whilst disposable products are convenient, reusable sanitary pads and tampons are becoming much more widely available. Although the initial cost can be off putting, over time they actually work out to be cheaper, and of course they're far more sustainable.

What are the benefits of reusable menstrual products?

1. Cloth pads are good for your body
Conventional disposable products can contain plastics, artificial fragrances, adhesives, and chemical gels – things you don't want next to one of the most sensitive parts of your body!
Cloth menstrual pads are free from irritating materials, so you can avoid unnecessary exposure to the synthetic ingredients in

disposable pads and tampons. They're available in a range of natural, sustainable materials such as organic cotton and bamboo.

2. Reusable menstrual pads are good for the planet

The average woman will use 12,000 to 16,000 disposable pads, liners, and tampons in her lifetime. That's a lot of waste! Plus, think of the manufacturing, shipping, and packaging impact over the years. Reusable menstrual pads last for years, helping you to reduce your impact on the environment and saving you from monthly trips to the shops. Many reusable brands are plastic and nylon free, and only use natural fibres.

3. Cloth pads are good for your budget.

Once you build your full set of reusable menstrual pads, you'll have reliable sanitary protection for years to come. Most reusable menstrual pads are made to last for five years, but many women report that their pads have lasted for much longer! Washable cloth pads are much more economical when compared to the cost of disposable products over your lifetime. Remember that the average girl just starting her period will use up to 16,000 disposable products in her lifetime. If she's buying a box of 20 tampons or pads at £2 per box, she'll throw away an average of £1500. It's kind of like equipping your kitchen with ceramic plates: it would be far more expensive (not to mention wasteful!) to continuously purchase disposable plates instead.

4. Reusable pads are comfortable

Reusable cloth pads are extremely soft and comfortable. You know that itchy, plastic-y feeling that comes from sitting in a disposable pad? It'll be a distant memory once you switch to soft, natural reusables. Many women also report reduced period pains when using natural, reusable products. Plastic filled products have a "wick" effect that draws menstrual flow from your body rather than allowing a slower, more natural flow.

Imagine if the only underwear you'd ever used or known about was made out of uncomfortable, chemical laden plastic and paper. That every week you had to go out and buy another 7 pairs of paper pants for the next week, that sometimes you couldn't afford them so you might skip school or work out of embarrassment. Crazy, right?

And yet this is what we're so used to with disposable sanitary products that most of us don't think twice about it.

Now imagine someone eventually telling you that there was a new product – natural cotton, washable pants that you could just wear, wash and wear again for years. Oh yeah, we already do that! Because plastic pants wouldn't make sense, and when you think about it, neither do disposables.

Making this one change in how you manage your periods will have a huge positive benefit in so many ways – for your health, the environment, your finances, and your comfort.

To find out more, simply search "reusable sanitary products" and get reading!

Written by Verity Venter

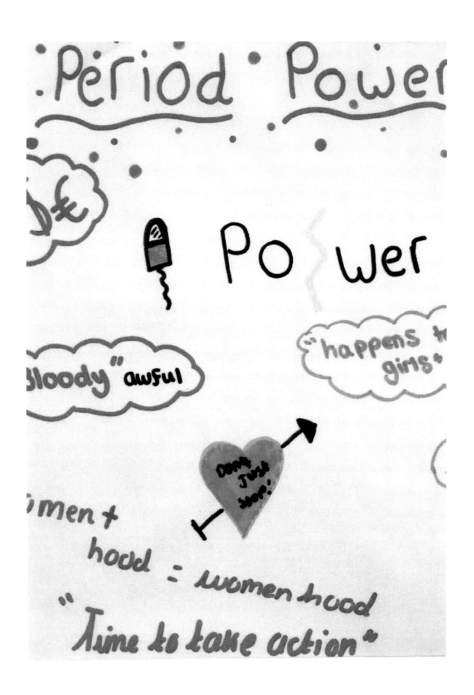

I have been awoken, threatened, and disturbed by my contracting womb whose walls flex and crumble like the rumble of distant thunder; far enough away to keep me still and to suppress what was to come.

The calm before the storm.

Again, I awake. A feint lightning flash burns me within, and my womb begins to wring and writhe like a molten mixer. It's a matter of minutes now; I know the cruel routine. I need weapons – paracetamol, ibuprofen but I CAN'T FIND THEM! Even then, they are so spitefully slow. My bowels move and empty like a frightened animal. Thick, hot blood pumps and saturates my pad. Waiting for pills to kick in, I can often vomit from the pain, only to watch the wretched chalky foam floating in the toilet bowl, like spume in a rock pool. They're no good to me now. I despair in the knowledge that it is still going to be an hour before I feel the pain subside. I take more pills. This time, I'm not sick. My hands are numbing with pins and needles, but I manage to boil the kettle because the only reliable comfort comes from my hot water bottle. She is hard to hold with dead hands and the kettle wobbles as I pour, but we are a team. Pain is still increasing, ever stronger and intense, so I pace and pant, pace, and pant. Sometimes, this happens in the day, and I can walk some place quiet (with luck) with a friend or my son. It helps to move; impossible alone – with my face drained so ashen-white and my legs so wobbly that people might think I am a junkie or something desperate and weak.

Now too tired to move, I go to bed and place my fluffy red hot water bottle in the womb-quake of my tummy, feeling the heat soak slowly through my flesh and pubis bone to the angry, contorting morass of muscle within. For half an hour or so, I feel the tides. I remember childbirth. I note that my right-hand ovary throbs and pulses in rhythm with my head and heart. I beg myself to stop torturing me. I sleep for a few seconds and then awake. I sleep. I awake. Then, slowly, ever so slowly, I sleep longer and longer. I am drained of a life force – someone pulled out that plug and it all ran away: a vampire's leftovers.

It is 4:21 a.m. I listen to my stomach, pop, and wheeze like lava in seawater, I surrender into the deepest most beautiful slumber.

Moon: 57.3%

Waning Gibbous
5 days past full
5 minutes past hell.

Written by Tracey Dixon

The Comedian:
Atchoo!
The forbidden sneeze.
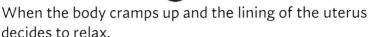
When the body cramps up and the lining of the uterus decides to relax.
Yep.
It's that time again.

The Emotional Eater:
The body becomes a balloon and the loving woman you knew becomes the devil herself.
The bath could be filled with tears and the local takeaways become concerned for your health.

The Aggressive Hulk:
The mind does weird things when your hormones are being pushed through your body. Somehow you are capable of things you never knew you were capable of. The once 10-stone sofa becomes a feather and somehow ends at the other end of the room during an argument.

The Reassuring Mother:
All of this trauma, and we do this so that one day we can bring someone into this world. To get that feeling that you have produced a miracle, that release of relief that you have created someone who will make a change.

The Motivational Speaker:
You did this, and you can do this. The stigma around periods is irrelevant compared to the significance of the reason why you have them. You're a woman and you SHOULD be proud.

Written by Trinnity Hulme

ACKNOWLEDGEMENTS

We, at Period Power, would like to thank the following for the support and funding which has allowed us to bring to fruition something which started as a little dream and, hopefully, has resulted in something we can all celebrate.

Safer Communities CIC for our initial funding. A special thank you to Denise Rowe.

Staffordshire Fire & Rescue Service for their continued support and faith in our work. A special thank you to Diane Dunlevey.

Olivia Lucas, working with the Staffordshire Youth Commission, for her collaboration in creating our initial social media posters.

Claire at SCVYS for supporting our successful bid for the Staffordshire County Council "Doing our Bit" fund which allowed us to move forward with the production of the book.

Staffordshire Community Foundation which enabled us to use some of our Tampon Tax funding to reach out to even more people. A special thank you to Leanne Macpherson.

North Staffordshire Press for their support from our very first meeting onwards. Without Malcolm Henson and Ellie Broadhurst, this project would not have happened so quickly and professionally.

However, our biggest thanks goes out to everyone for their factual, inspirational, funny and honest responses to #AllThingsPeriods. We appreciate the time given to compose and illustrate your journey with menstruation. This book has been made possible by the contributions of those who share a journey. The path we take is one that takes us from child to woman. We honour and stand in solidarity with everyone who shares this journey.